OLD FATHER

the story teller

— SPIRITUAL SUN SYMBOL
    to light all paths of life
EYES — to see more clearly
MOUTH — to speak truthfully

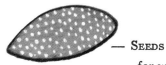

— COURSE
    four directions - -
        Paths of the earth to
           reach every trail

— SEEDS
    for wisdom and new thoughts

— WRIST to bend
    Tolerance towards others
— ARM — Strength, Courage
    and Character
    To raise above oneself

— SPLIT LEAF sharing new
    knowledge with others

HAND — Charity and Love
    Extend to others help and
    kindness

                PABLITA VELARDE

Pablita Velarde, most noted Indian woman painter in the U.S., was born Sept. 18, 1918, in Santa Clara Pueblo, northwest of Santa Fe, New Mexico. The Santa Claras speak Tewa, as do Tesuque, San Ildefonso, San Juan, Nambe (mostly Mexicanized), and Pojoaque (practically extinct).

OLD FATHER

the story teller
By PABLITA VELARDE

DALE STUART KING, publisher
Globe, Arizona
1960

Printed in the United States of America
By Northland Press, Flagstaff, Arizona

L. C. Catalog Card No. 60-16407

Dedicated to
HELEN and HERBY

About Pablita
and her Legends

From her secure niche as a painter of renown Pablita has ventured on this excursion into writing. In her own words, she "thought it would be a good thing if an Indian wrote an Indian book", and so she has written one. That is Pablita, self-reliant in the complex task of bridging two cultures.

Daughter of Herman and Marianita Chavarria Velarde, Pablita was born in the Tewa-speaking pueblo of Santa Clara, New Mexico, and lived there until she was sent to nearby Santa Fe, at the age of six, for schooling. First she attended St. Catherine's school, then the Santa Fe Indian school, entering seventh grade there in 1932. This was a year of good omen for Indian painting, for it saw the beginning of the Indian school's art class under the direction of Dorothy Dunn, graduate of the Chicago Art Institute, whose years in Santa Fe were devoted to the guidance and encouragement of many young Indian artists.

After graduation from high school in 1936 Pablita taught in Santa Clara day school. In the fall of 1938 horizons were broadened when Mr. and Mrs. Ernest Thompson Seton took her on a four-month tour of the midwest, eastern and southern United States.

In the summer of 1939 she was commissioned by Archaeologist Dale Stuart King of the Southwestern National Monuments Office of the National Park Service to paint illustrations for the ethnological room in the museum at Bandelier National Monument, an assignment executed most commendably by the young artist. The study and research involved in this work doubtlessly contributed to the authenticity of her painting, past and present, of Indian subjects.

Pablita has exhibited widely and successfully, collecting awards and honors from the annual Indian Ceremonial at Gallup and the Philbrook Art Center at Tulsa, Oklahoma, among others.

13

She is one of the dozen or so Indian artists who have been decorated with the Palme Academique by the French government in recognition of their exhibits at the Gallup Ceremonial.

At present living in Albuquerque with her daughter, Helen, and son, Herbert, Jr., children of Pablita and her former husband, Herbert Oliver Hardin, she is active in art associations and other community affairs, and is called upon frequently to show her legend paintings and tell the stories they picture. As she sits dressed in colorful Indian costume, summoning in charming accent the myths of America's furthermost past and offering them like corn pollen to today, she is an impressive symbol of the Pueblo Indian in transition. Her great talent is a genuine expression of the environment which was hers by birth and a rare enrichment of the wider environment into which she has blended.

Pablita's earthcolor paintings are done with a technique perfected by her, beginning with the gathering of stones and clays of varied hues. These she powders between **metate** and **mano,** mixing and applying according to methods she has evolved. Her technique in this ancient medium (the Old Ones used earth colors) is typically Indian, yet highly individual—and such a contribution is uncommon for the very good reason that pueblo heritage is communal and traditional.

Lacking qualifications as an art critic myself, it seems pertinent to quote this evaluation made by Dorothy Dunn, from an article in **El Palacio,** journal of the Museum of New Mexico:

"Pablita Velarde's one man show . . . reveals the strength, depth, and versatility of this young Santa Clara woman as artist. This is not the work of a follower, but of a pace-setter.

"One might well predict that someday this (Old Father, the Story Teller) will be considered a great American painting. It has components of very fine art indeed— a profound concept, an illusion convincingly projected through ingenious composition, controlled color, and markedly individual technique. Moreover, it opens to view events and ideas heretofore unknown outside the

Tewa world. It is in fact a new, yet related, version of the old life-linked legends and beliefs of people everywhere . . . By such art as this, people are drawn together and are given to know that 'theirs' and 'ours' are basically the same."

Because of this book we are richer when we look at Orion and see Long Sash as well. As for the other legends, the warm kinship between "theirs" and "ours" is of course even more apparent in the story of Turkey Girl, the universal Cinderella daydream. And Sad Eyes has many cousins, from Romulus and Remus to Tarzan. The story of the Enchanted Hunter becomes more fascinating when it is known that the action describes a psychological rather than a physical journey; it suggests a Faust with sales resistance. Butterfly Boy is a favorite legend of Pablita's, recording as it does the plight of the artist in most cultures.

Only "The First Twins", the Koshares, seem strange to European-based concepts. Although "we" recognize that clownpaint often covers a noble soul, we do not subscribe generally to a clown-leader combination. That the Indian did so is intriguing, considering his immense racial dignity, and one may be sure that his reasons for it were valid and deep.

I, for one, thank him for food for thought. And I thank my friend Pablita for her delightful presentations in paint and prose.

D. Hancock

Albuquerque, New Mexico
November, 1959

Foreword

Indian legends are not always easy to understand, for small details are very likely to carry much meaning. For the non-Indian reader I have tried to simplify and explain some things more than Old Father did for his listeners.

I was one of the fortunate children of my generation who were probably the last to hear stories firsthand from Great-grandfather or Grandfather. I treasure that memory, and I have tried to preserve it in this book so that my children as well as other people may have a glimpse of what used to be.

Credit is due my father, Herman Velarde, of Santa Clara Pueblo, for refreshing my memory on many points. I am grateful for it, and for having such a wonderful man as my father. All I can say here is **kuda whyo-ha,** thanks, in our Tewa tongue.

My **kuda whyo-ha** to friends for their help and encouragement, and to my children, Helen and Herby, for their love and **faith.**

P.V.

Albuquerque, New Mexico
November 15, 1959

Contents

An example of authentic Indian symbolism:
    Pablita's design for a colophon   5

About Pablita and her legends, by D. Hancock   13

Foreword   17
    Old Father painting   23

The Stars   25

Sad Eyes   33
    Sad Eyes painting   34

Enchanted Hunter   39
    Enchanted Hunter painting   40

Turkey girl   45
    Turkeys preening girl's hair   46
    Turkeys making girl bathe   48
    Giant turkey wing shields girl   50

Butterfly Boy   53

First Twins   57
    First Twins painting   61

Index   65

OLD FATHER
the story teller

Ancient village in the right hand corner. Old Father sits in the plaza as he points to each constellation to tell his story.

Above, the constellation Orion (Long Sash) leads the way, right to left, across the Milky Way (Endless Trail). They slide off to the center of the earth, left to right, follow the trail of the mole to Mother Spider, Eagle, Bear, Coyote, Lion and Turtle.

The step design symbolizes the four sacred mountains. The colors signify the directions: white, north; yellow, west; blue, east; and red, south. Small spruce trees stand on each peak.

22

THE STARS

Many stars made bright holes in the clear, cold, autumn sky. In the village plaza a fire danced and children danced around it. They were happy and excited because Old Father was in the village and would begin tonight to tell them the winter's stories.

"Tell us a story, tell us a story." They loved Old Father and he loved them and understood them. His kindness made a warmth like the fire. He laughed and asked "What kind of a story?", and a tiny voice came tumbling, "Why are some stars brighter than all the others? And why don't they ever fall where we can find them?"

The children settled around the fire as Old Father gazed up at the stars with a faraway smile. Pointing first toward Orion in the east, he said:

THAT is "Long Sash", the guide of our ancestors; he led our people to this beautiful land where we now live. Our people followed him without question, for he was a great warrior who had won many battles. He had grown tired of seeing misery all around him, his own people suffering because of the cruel ruler they had lived under for so many years. During his battles he

25

had been in distant lands, and when he told his people about these places they asked him to take them there. They were determined to end their suffering by going away to a new land.

He tried to discourage them, telling them they had nothing to take along. He warned them of the hardships, the sickness, and the deaths they would face, but they were determined people, and in the end he could not refuse them.

They traveled with empty stomachs and scant clothing. Many died from hunger and disease, but they continued on and on. Long Sash taught them to hunt for their food, to make clothing from animal skins and bird feathers. After a time he led them into a land where no man, not even he, had been. It was daylight all the time, and they rested only when they were too weary to travel any more. Many children were born, and some died, but the brave spirit of these people kept them going.

Old Father paused to look around him. He saw all the children were gazing upward as if the stars, gleaming like mica, had hypnotized them. Waving his hand across the sky Old Father raised the pitch of his voice, bringing the children out of their trance. They followed him, wide-eyed and open-mouthed.

"See that milky white belt across the middle of the sky?"

"Yes," they all answered at once.

"Well," continued Old Father, "that is the Endless Trail they were traveling on. In time, some of the people became doubtful and hard to reason with, and violence began to show itself here and there. Thereupon Long Sash decided that force was to be used on no one, that those who wished to follow him could come, and those who wanted to turn back could do so. In order to give every one an opportunity to rest and make his own decision, he had them camp on the spot. It was time for many of the women to bear their babies.

"See those two big bright stars (Gemini) to the north of Long Sash?" Old Father waited for an answer, but when none came he smiled and continued:

26

They are stars of decision. We must all make choices between forward or backward, good or bad. They mark the trail where Long Sash told his people, "If we choose to go forward, it will be a good choice, for the lives of the young stretch long before them. Choose the road back and you know what torture you will live. We have our signs ahead of us; let us not close our eyes, to see only the darkness!

It did not take long for the people to decide to follow their leader. They all went on with lighter hearts and greater hopes. Long Sash sang loudly as he led his people on what seemed an endless journey. He hoped they would reach their destination soon, but he had prepared his people well, he had taught them patience, tolerance, and love for one another. Yet for some reason there was an emptiness in his own soul and he could not understand the reason why.

He himself was growing tired of the long wandering, and when he was by himself he wept in despair. He began to feel strange beings around him, and to hear unfamiliar voices. Not understanding these things, his first thought was that he must be losing his mind, but he was determined that he would lead his people to safety before anything happened to him. While he was resting he began talking aloud, and his people thought he was talking to them, and they gathered around him.

His voice was strange: "My fathers and my mothers, wherever you are, hear me, give me your guidance and give me strength to find our home. My people are tired now and I am not young as I once was. Give me wisdom and strength to decide for them, and give me an omen, give me an omen!"

The people looked at each other fearfully, feeling the need for someone stronger than Long Sash to depend upon. They looked at him, who was now asleep. They discussed what he had said and wondered about the unseen beings with whom he had spoken. They became afraid of him, and when he awoke he sensed that something was troubling his people, so he gathered them about him and told them he had had a dream with many omens in it. He told them the most difficult part of their journey was over;

traveling would be easier for the rest of the trip. He told them of the unseen beings and the voices he had sensed, and commanded that they be addressed as "Fathers and Mothers", and that the people ask for their aid whenever the need for help was felt. "Always have faith in them, for they will answer you with their blessings. I am not sick of mind. Now my mind is clearer than it has ever been. I will leave my headdress here as a symbol to all the others who may need a reminder of the greater spirits."

Old Father again pointed to the heavens toward the cluster of seven bright stars in the shape of a bonnet (Cancer), saying, "That represents the war bonnet of Long Sash." The children shifted a little and closed their mouths, dry by this time. He continued:

As they traveled they learned many new ways to carry loads. At first they bore their belongings on their backs, but now, with more babies to be carried, the younger men teamed up in pairs to drag the loads on poles. See the three stars (Leo) north of the headdress? They represent love, tolerance and understanding, and were personified by two young men dragging their load and saving their people from worse hardship.

After a long time they came into darkness and everyone was afraid again, but their leader kept on, following a bright light coming through a very small opening. (**sipapu** in Hopi; **sipo-pede** in Tewa). From somewhere they heard something digging and scratching. Still following the bright light they came closer to the noise, and when they reached the opening they found a little mole digging away. Long Sash thanked the small creature for helping them to find the opening, but the mole only replied, "Go, and when you again find my sign, you will have found your home." They found a cord hanging and climbed toward the opening.

Through the opening Long Sash saw Old Spider Woman, busy weaving, and he asked permission to enter. Replied Old Spider Woman, "You are welcome to pass through my house. Do not destroy anything and I will help you find your way out and show you the direction to take. When you see my sign again, you will have found your home." Long Sash thanked her, but he could not understand at the time what she meant.

28

Continuing on their way they came to a very cold, beautiful land to the north where they rested for many years. Some stayed to make their homes, for they were tired of moving. Long Sash told his people, "This is the land of ice and snow, and your helper is the bear, for he is big and powerful, as one must be in order to live here. Those who wish to continue I will lead, for we have not yet found any signs of the mole and spider."

The people asked Long Sash why he did not follow the sun to the west, and they went in the direction of the setting sun and came to a place where the land was hot and dry. They rested here for many years, some of them staying to make it their home.

Long Sash was restless, so he prepared to leave, saying, "This is the land of the coyote, the sun is hot and the air is dry, the wind echoes the wails of the creatures who live in the surrounding hills. It has its own beauty, but you who remain here will follow the ways of the coyote and wander about aimlessly preying on whatever you find on your way. Those who wish to follow me will go with me to the land of the sunrise where we will seek the sign of the spider and the mole."

Once more they traveled, this time until they reached the land to the east. There they found tall trees, plenty of water, and earth covered with green wherever they looked. Here indeed, they thought, was the land promised by the two prophetic creatures. Here life was easier and many of the people were happy to make this their home, despite the ever present danger of wild beasts who often pounced upon them. The seasons were short.

Still they had not found the signs of the mole and spider, so Long Sash said to his people, "This is indeed a beautiful land where game is plentiful, but the seasons of warmth are short and the changes are too swift. This is the land of the cougar. He is dangerous and unpredictable as the seasons, so we will go to the south in search of the signs."

So, sad because brothers and sisters had parted, but with hope in their hearts and faith in their leader, they again set out until they came to a land in the south where the seasons were long, food was easier to find, and there was not the danger from lurking beasts. Still they were not sure this was their home, for they had not found the signs they were seeking, even though they searched all over the land of the south, to the borders of the lands of the bear, the coyote, and the cougar.

Long Sash called again for help from his spiritual ancestors, praying that they would again show him a sign. He felt low in spirit, but he taught his followers how to talk from their hearts, and how to find happiness in their misery, and how to read signs. From him they learned a new way of life, guided by a new belief. Many of our ancient ceremonials born of that belief are still with us, but many others have passed with time.

After Long Sash's communication with the spirits of his forefathers, a great bird flew overhead and circled the people four times before dropping two feathers from its tail. Falling to the ground, one feather pointed in the direction of the coyote, while the other pointed to the people. Long Sash then declared, "Here is our sign from our powerful messenger, the eagle. He tells us to follow in this direction!"

When they came to the new land they found it to have seasons wet and dry, hot and cold, with good soil and bad. There was game, but it was hard to get. Here and there they found little scratches or tracks, but they had not found the mole as they had expected to do. However, close to the banks of a muddy river they found an ugly little creature with a very rough skin and on his back a stone-like shell. He made the tracks of a mole, yet he was not a mole. Long Sash studied him for a long time before he exclaimed, "Look, he carries his home with him and is protected by it at all times because when he is drawn up inside it he looks and rolls like a rock. He travels slowly, as we have done. On his back we can see plainly that he carries the sign of the spider; and when he moves, his feet make tracks like those of the mole."

This made the people very happy, for now they were certain they had found their homeland here where we are today. We move about a little now and then but we will never leave this land, for this is where we belong.

The signs in the sky will always be there to guide us. Long Sash (Orion) is still up there leading many lost tribes over the

Endless Trail (Milky Way). The Twins (Gemini), the two stars of decision, are choices we always have. There is the headdress (Cancer) of Long Sash, reminding us of his spiritual guidance; there is the team of young men dragging their load (Leo) to remind us of love, tolerance, and understanding. The big star (North Star) which guided our ancestors through the darkness is still there.

See those seven bright stars (Big Dipper) that form an animal with its tail hanging downward? That is Long Tail. Each star in this group represents a sign given us by one of the creatures I told you of, the mole, the spider, the bear, the coyote, the cougar, the eagle and the turtle.

Look at the four high mountain peaks around you: to the north, Bear mountain (Taos Mountains); to the west (Mt. Taylor), the Coyote; to the east (Sangre de Cristo Mountains), the Cougar; and to the south, the Turtle (Sandia) mountains. Within these boundaries our people found their home.

Why don't you find stars after they fall? Well, Long Sash is playing a game, and he catches them before they reach you!

* * * * *

The children sat and gazed upward, still hearing the voices of the past, as Old Father rose and stretched, saying, "I will pass here again, with other stories. Go home to your parents and sleep well. **Songe-de-ho,** goodbye!"

31

SAD EYES

At sunrise a Deer Dance had begun, and most of the children had been awake since long before dawn. Still they chattered around the evening fire, asking Old Father endless questions about the day's exciting ceremony. Said Old Father,

WHENEVER **you hear** the early morning call of the Deer Dance ceremony you are hearing the echo of a song once sung to the deer by a boy who loved them.

It was pinyon harvesting time, and everyone in the village was camping on the high mesa near Puye. Men, women, and children started out early at dawn. A girl among them was expecting a child, and being young and inexperienced, she wandered deep into the woods, and there she bore her son. Frightened, she made her way back to camp but could not remember which direction she had taken, and although a search was made, the child could not be found.

A family of deer came down to the canyon to drink at evening time. Father deer was leading as usual, with mother following, then the young one. The old buck sensed something strange, and after sniffing the air he approached a clump of bushes, where

33

Pablita Velarde

he found the little human boy. He called the other two deer and they all sniffed the child and licked him with their tongues. Mother deer said she would nurse the boy, and while she fed him she began to love this little human child and made plans to carry him home. This she did by laying him across the father deer's antlers, and in this manner they carried him with them wherever they wandered.

As time went by the child grew and was happy with life. He was as wild as the animals and as swift-footed. He knew he was different but did not know how he came to be so. He understood the ways of the deer, for he was one of them. He knew the changes of the seasons and became aware of the dangers around him.

One year, when the leaves had changed and fallen, he was saddened for the first time in his life, because his deer brother whom he loved very much was missing. He went to look for his brother, and during his search he came near a camp where he saw beings like himself sitting around a fire, making noises. He could not understand why they sat so close to the fire, for to him fire was dangerous! He heard one of them lifting his voice above the others, and it made him want to do the same thing. He tried it, but he was heard and seen by the men, and soon he was running through the thicket to escape, which he did easily by outrunning his pursuers.

When he came back to the cave where he lived he told Father and Mother Deer what he had seen, and tried to sing the song. Although they did not understand him, they listened and approved. It became a familiar sound to them to hear the boy sing as he rode on the back of the father deer.

At the village there was excitement at the news the men told of seeing a wild boy in the woods. It was decided to hunt him down, as he might have been the cause of their many hunting failures the past few seasons. The first tries were disappointing; they could not locate the boy or even a deer. At last they encircled the water hole and sat in wait for the deer to come for their daily drink. They heard singing and saw a herd of deer coming, with the boy riding on the back of the biggest and oldest buck in the herd!

As the boy jumped off and lay flat on the ground to drink, the hunters closed in and captured him. They took him to the village and locked him in a room with a very small opening, and he was bewildered and very frightened.

He could not eat the food given him. All his life he had eaten roots, berries, and nuts and had drunk milk from mother deer with new fawns. His stomach pained, but still he would not eat. His eyes grew sadder every day.

One evening he heard voices as a woman outside his room begged the guard to allow her to see the boy. At first the guard would not listen, and became angry with her, and pushed her out of the way. She fell, and her eyes filled with tears. Her eyes had such sadness in them, the guard felt very sorry he had been brutal, and he helped her up and let her enter the room, with a last warning that the boy was wild and might harm her.

As she entered she saw the boy crouching in a corner and she knelt beside him and studied his features. A deep feeling drew her to him, but when she lifted her hand to touch him he sprang out of reach. As they gazed steadily at one another, the sadness in his eyes seemed to be asking something of her. She knew the strange boy was miserable, and she smiled gently at him. His expression did not change, but after a time he did not seem to be afraid of her.

After that, the woman was allowed to stay with the boy. She made him sandals, and a kilt, and when she dressed him she was pleased to see he was a handsome young man. She showed him how to tan animal hides and to use the bone awl and sinews of animals for sewing. She made a quiver out of the skin of a lynx, taught him how to make arrows with flint tips, and brought him a bow. He even learned to say a few words, just as he had learned from the deer their way of talking.

He sometimes smiled at the woman now, but his eyes did not lose their sadness. Most of the day he stood at the small window

36

humming his song, looking up at the fog clouds, the cloud flowers, on top of the mountain. Slowly the woman came to know he would never be happy with people. She thought of how she herself had often gone alone to the mountain and found peace there, feeling near to the Great One as she listened to the mountain's breath-sound. She promised herself that when the time was right she would help the boy find his way back where he belonged.

In the mountains the deer had missed the boy, too. In dangerous attempts to find him some had lost their lives. As time passed they thought his life, too, must have been lost, and more sadness came into their eyes.

One day the woman was allowed to take the boy for a walk, the belief being that he had forgotten the deer. They walked toward the mountains, the boy's hand held tightly in hers, and when they turned to come back she saw the boy's eyes fill with tears. **"Ahi, ahi,** what can I do," she chanted softly, and she let his hand go. As he walked away from her he was singing his song, and the woman knew this time it was for her.

Now it is she who looks from her window up at the mountain, but her eyes are not sad. She has just finished a water jug, on it a new design, "The House of the Deer". To her it means the dwelling place of the spirit deer, a place where he has eternal freedom, and this brings her happiness for the strange boy.

As you know, we still use her design on ceremonial ollas.

ENCHANTED HUNTER

Old Father sat smoking a corn husk tobacco cigarette while the children around the fireplace waited patiently for him to begin a story. He was thinking of how each one must learn to awaken to his senses, to know himself as he is, good or bad, weak or strong; of how one must be alert, guarding against bodily harm and against the evil that can disturb the **e-ve-hanuh**, the inner self, but it is hard for children to understand.

Finally he began, "You know it is not good to be out late in the night, don't you?" The children nodded. "It is the darkness," he said, "that makes us afraid, if we do not understand it."

AT one **time** there lived a young man, quiet, a hard worker, and an excellent hunter. He generously shared his game with others, but envious people wished him evil.

These evil ones told him that the beautiful sister of one of them admired him and wished to see him at a special place. They said he would find her if he went there and listened for her song.

Although the hunter did not trust these men, thoughts of the beautiful girl were strong and he asked himself, "What can a woman do to me that can harm me?"

He went to the meeting place, but when he arrived she was not there. He sat down and looked about him and noticed that four deep canyons came together at this point. That was strange —he had passed here before and had not seen the canyons.

After a long wait, he arose to go, but a whirlwind demon blinded him with dust. At the same time he heard a beautiful song echoing from the canyons.

Singing was always the chief magic for creating anything, good or bad, and this song cast a spell over him so that he became helpless even to think.

He turned aimlessly and saw Spider Woman walking up the foot trail toward him, carrying a bundle of twigs. Old Spider Woman, although one of the cloud people, was very close to her earth children. She guessed the young hunter's trouble, and chewing one of her curing herbs, she rubbed her spittle on his temples. The hunter immediately recovered from his spell.

She warned that the voice was that of a beautiful witch in the third canyon, gave him a pouch with some herbs in it, and told him how and when to use them.

As he thanked her, he tried to quiet the wild beating of his pulse. He felt as if he were running. He seemed to be two persons instead of one, with voices quarreling inside, one warning him of dangers, and the other saying here was new game to hunt.

Then the song drew him to the deepest part of Flint Knife canyon. But then it sounded from the top of the opposite cliff— across the swift and muddy river and the jagged rocks.

Fear took hold of him and he wanted to turn and run back, but his hand pulled one of the herbs from the pouch and he chewed it, then rubbed his body from head to foot. He felt stronger, and as he proceeded to cross the river he discovered that the muddy water cleared and the strong current calmed.

At the cliff top he sank down exhausted. His new sandals, woven of hide and feathers, were in shreds. Soon it would be too dark to go any farther, and he listened for the song. All was quiet. The prairie in front of him was filled with cactus and weeds with thorns. There were no birds in the sky, a strange ugly smell drifted on the air, and he knew these were signs of snakes.

As he walked slowly across the flats he saw many poisonous insects and countless kinds of snakes. His body moved straight ahead, but as if another's soul directed it.

Consciousness returned to him sharply, and he thought he had slept. For how long? The sun was setting. He stood up and to his amazement found he was on the far side of the flats, without any recollection of crossing them. He noticed a small village with thin smoke coming from one of the dwellings, and he hurried toward it, racing the darkness.

He asked entrance and an old woman let him in. He heard queer noises coming from another room, but the old woman watched him so closely he did not inquire. He knew she was one without a heart! Danger tightened his scalp—was this the witches' village?

The old woman set before him a bowl of stew. He pinched the meat, to offer a bit of it as thanksgiving to the Great Spirit, and as he did so it turned into a human heart! He knew well that eating it would have changed him into an evil one. People who want witches' powers turn themselves into witches by eating human hearts, completing their initiation by consuming the heart of the person they love the most.

Quickly the hunter chewed an herb and spit into the bowl, and at this the old woman rushed to climb out of the room, and in her panic fell off the top of the house!

Through a small opening in the wall he peered into the next room and beheld other evil ones going through their rites. He noticed that the only other opening into the room was through the roof. Rubbing an herb on his flint knife he scratched a circle around the opening, then hurried to the roof and repeated the act—Spider Woman had told him this would imprison witches. After it was done he began to feel safe and he lay down and slept.

Out of habit he went out before sunrise and gave offerings to the Great One. Then he called down to the beautiful witch through the roof opening. She begged forgiveness, but he refused to release her until she gave him the plumes which endowed her with evil powers. To be sure that they were her's and not someone else's, he spit herb juice on the plumes, and set fire to them. If they did not burn, she had lied, and would be imprisoned forever; if they burned, she would return with him, but without her evil power. They did catch fire, and ashes fell on the upturned faces of the other evil ones, destroying them all except the young witch.

The hunter sang a short chant and with a peaceful heart started back the way he had come. The witch followed—across the same horrible flats—where she was bitten by the snakes and insects. She had to slide down the canyon wall and was almost torn to pieces by the swift rocky river in Flint Knife canyon.

In his village the sun was ending another day. His neighbors were surprised he brought back no game. Taking his stand in the center of the village, the hunter sang his song: "One who was lost in sleep, one who was lost in sleep, took me far, far away."

The listeners did not understand his meaning. As they wondered, they saw the young witch approach, still following the hunter, walking as one whose senses were not with her. And as they watched, she fainted into eternal sleep.

*   *   *   *   *

"When we can face the darkness without fear," said Old Father, "we can sing the hunter's song. The mind will play us tricks if we let it!"

TURKEY GIRL

A little girl asked the old man with the kind face, "Old Father, are there any little girls in the mountains?" Old Father answered, "There is Turkey Girl." The child munched parched corn and waited for him to continue. "If you don't stop eating so much parched corn you might turn into a little turkey yourself!" He smiled as he went on:

LIVING with her foster mother at Shupinna was a young girl. For a livelihood they depended on a flock of turkeys which the girl had to take out every day to forage for food. She was fond of the turkeys, and found her only happiness in talking to them each day. Her foster mother was a cruel woman who had despised the child from the time she took her in, after her parents had been killed by an enemy tribe.

Since no one could remember the name given to the girl by her parents, and since she had been with her turkeys from the first days she could walk, it was natural that she should be called "Turkey Girl."

One day after she had reached her early maidenhood, a ceremonial was to be held at Puye. As Turkey Girl had never been

beyond the boundaries of Shupinna and had never seen any kind of celebration, she asked her foster mother to take her along. The hateful woman, who cared only for the work she could get from Turkey Girl, sneered, "You go to the ceremonial with me? Look at you! Your hair is crawling with lice and your dress is dirty. Turkey Girl! Why, the very name you have makes you smell like one. No, you can't come with me. Go and tend to your turkeys!"

With that she left for Puye and the celebration, while poor miserable Turkey Girl returned to her birds. After she got them to their grazing place she sat down and cried, pouring out words of grief between sobs. The turkeys listened, then one of the older birds gobbled, and at this signal they began to pull her matted hair and pick out the lice.

Upon being attacked in this manner, she thought, "Now even the birds don't like me. Let them kill me, for I want to die."

The turkeys tried to be gentle in their task, but it was not easy. After finishing, they all headed for the river, and because she feared what her foster mother would do if she lost one bird, Turkey Girl followed them. When they reached the river's edge she stooped over the water to drink, whereupon the turkeys pushed her in and stood guard over her until she was bathed clean.

She watched them pick her dirty, ragged dress to pieces, and asked what she was to wear, reminding them that she had no other garment. Again the oldest bird gobbled, and another turkey knocked a stick into the pool. Grabbing the stick, Turkey Girl struck the oldest turkey, and he instantly dropped a beautiful new **manta** (dress). When one of the other birds came rushing toward the **manta**, Turkey Girl thought he meant to destroy it, and again she struck out with the stick, causing the turkey to drop a brilliant red woven sash.

Two more birds came rushing toward her, and she thought, "They are angry with me for hitting their brothers and they will surely peck me to death!" She struck at them until her stick broke, then closed her eyes in fear, but as everything suddenly

47

became quiet she opened her eyes to see where the turkeys had gone.

There before her were six turkeys holding out the new apparel they had dropped. She begged them to forgive her, promising that as long as she lived she would never hurt them again. They all gobbled and let her out of the water.

After she had dressed in her new **manta,** sash and moccasins, two birds gave her strings of coral for necklaces and blue bands to hold back her hair, now long, clean and shining black. She was beautiful!

The turkeys looked pleased. They gobbled and gobbled, motioning for her to go. Hearing some travelers passing, she ran to see who they were, and when they saw the lovely girl they asked her to come along to the celebration. She looked back at her turkeys and thought she heard the oldest one telling her to go, so she went.

When she got to Puye the ceremonial dancing had begun, and after watching for awhile she realized that everyone was staring in her direction. She did not understand that it was her beauty they were admiring. Even her foster mother was gaping, without recognizing her.

Soon all the young men and even some of the older ones were asking her name and where she was from. Some offered her gifts, while others began to quarrel, and when the fuss erupted into a fight, Turkey Girl became frightened and decided to get back to Shupinna as fast as her feet would take her. The crowd followed her for a distance, but her years with the turkey herd had made her nimble-footed and she soon outran them. She was still trying to understand the crowd's behavior when she got back to her turkeys, and sat down on a rock to tell them her story.

While she was talking, her foster mother appeared (the celebration having been ended by the fighting) and when she spied the girl who had caused the disturbance, she asked, "What are you doing with my turkeys? Where is Turkey Girl?" When Turkey Girl answered, the woman recognized her and ran back to tell

the quarreling men that the beautiful girl they had been fighting over was none other than a black-hearted witch called Turkey Girl!

Hearing this, the men started out to find Turkey Girl and kill her, as was customary for all witches. However, the turkeys sensed danger to their mistress and led her away up the high mountains to the west, toward a sacred cave on the mountain top.

They had almost reached the cave when they heard shouts from close behind, "There is the witch, kill her!" As the pursuers aimed their stone hatchets, rocks and arrows, a weird, beautiful turkey wing of monstrous size arose, hiding Turkey Girl and her flock, giving them a few precious seconds to enter the cave of shrines, into a better land.

After the girl and her turkeys disappeared, the giant wing vanished also, and when the foster mother and her accomplices approached, all they found were turkey tracks on the ground and echoes of gobbling coming from the canyon walls. Since that time the mountain has been called "Turkey Track Mountain" by our people. They say many unbelievers have hunted there, but all have returned disappointed, with the same story, "We heard turkeys gobbling in the canyons, but all we found were turkey tracks!"

BUTTERFLY BOY

Making his way slowly between villages, Old Father stopped to rest under a cottonwood tree as ancient and rugged as he. While he rested, the last yellow leaf floated down and settled on his shoulder. He laughed to see how much the leaf looked like a butterfly, and thought it was a good sign, for butterflies mean happiness. Tonight at the next village, he decided, he would tell this story:

THE child, Pu-gah-nu-nu, was not like the other boys. Instead of running and shouting with the others he liked to sit with his back against a cool adobe wall and watch blue cloud shadows move across the golden plain and climb the painted mesa. He was a dreamer, and the village people thought him lazy and even a little stupid.

As **Pu-gah-nu-nu** grew older he had to do his share of the work of the village, planting and harvesting, hunting and gathering wood, but his real life went on within himself.

One day when the elders had sent him and the other boys out to harvest corn, he seemed more awkward than usual. His companions teased him because he was not strong and challenged him

53

to races across the field. If only he could get away, go off by himself and rest, then he might think of something he could do to teach those tormentors a lesson! When the work was done, he escaped to sit alone on the river bank, pretending not to hear the others calling him as they started home shouting their songs.

"Why can't I be like them?" he thought. "What a miserable person I am." He thought of each boy separately and envied each, some for strength, some for happy hearts, and even some for knavery and cunning ways.

Just then a butterfly flew past. Captivated as usual by beauty, he stood up, and his troubles dropped from him. Swiftly he followed the lovely thing, thinking only to hold his eyes on its brightness, forgetting time and distance. Suddenly, without knowing how he had come there, he found himself in a glade of such splendor that he stopped and rubbed his eyes. All around him magnificent mountains rose like guards. Rainbows gleamed above and sunbeams fell through the rainbows. Here before the young man's eyes was all the beauty he had ever imagined, and he knew he had been led to the place where the gods stayed.

He looked around for the butterfly and with great reverence he beheld it change into an **O-ku-wah,** a Cloud Person. The Kachina touched him on the shoulders and breathed into his eyes, ears, nose and mouth. He could not remember that the **O-ku-wah** uttered any sound before vanishing as suddenly as he had appeared. But when the butterfly became visible again, leading him away, the wind began to sing, and as he sang with it, words were put into his singing to describe the beauty he had seen. And he danced a gliding step as the butterfly led him home.

Pu-gah-nu-nu loved his people; his thoughts were gentle toward them even though they had often made fun of him. He wanted to share with them these wonderful things taught him by the **O-ku-wah.**

"**Pu-gah-nu-nu** has been dreaming again," they said. But he carried them along with him by the happiness in his face, and a great ceremony was arranged so that he could show them what he had learned.

54

Word of the Butterfly Dance spread, and people from other villages came to watch. They felt their hearts lifted upward as **Pu-gah-nu-nu** danced with a beautiful maiden the gliding steps and the gestures of his pursuit of the butterfly. And as he taught them the songs he had learned, which make up a prayer for guidance, they were filled with thanksgiving for this young man they had sometime scorned.

As the ceremony ended a mist gathered around **Pu-gah-nu-nu**, making him sacred. Then two Butterfly Kachinas came to dance away with him until he disappeared, leaving with his people the blessing of the Butterfly Dance, a reminder of the happiness to be found in the love of beauty.

55

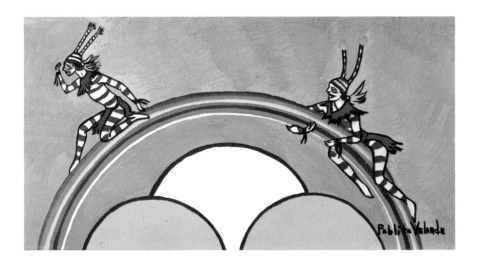

FIRST TWINS

When the snows had gone Old Father came to the village to take part in the Thawing-out ceremony, and he told the children this story:

IN another village a long time ago there lived an old couple. They had no children of their own, although they had prayed every day to the Great One for a child.

Early one morning as they returned home from giving offering to the Great Spirit they heard the weak crying of a baby. Both wondered if they had really heard the sound or if it were just wishful thinking. The old man walked toward the woodpile to gather some wood for the old woman's outdoor fireplace, toward which she had turned. As he bent over the woodpile he saw a tiny baby lying there! He called to the old woman, but to her own astonishment she had found in the ashes of the fireplace a tiny baby boy! They lifted the babies and turned at the same moment to show each other what they had found.

The sun was just rising over the mountains, and holding the babies toward it they silently prayed for care and protection of the children. Then Grandfather went off to report the finding of

57

the children to the men who governed the village, leaving Grandmother at home praying they would be allowed to keep the babies. In four days they would know, for, according to custom, if no one claimed the children in that time and no other family wanted them they might remain with the finders.

Surely, she thought, this was no ordinary thing, it was the answer to their prayers. She wondered for a minute if they were too old to care for children, but immediately scolded herself for doubting the wise ones who had blessed her with these fine boys. Surely they would be allowed to stay, and so it was. After four anxious days, such joy and happiness filled the old ones' hearts—the children were theirs to keep with them always!

As the years passed, the boys grew strong and happy. Grandfather taught them all the things young men should know—planting, harvesting and hunting—and they learned fast, and took over all of the old man's work. Grandmother taught them how to take care of their bodies and also how to avoid the evil ones.

Even when very young the twins would pick wild flowers to bring home for Grandmother, and when they were teased about it by the other boys, they would laughingly say they ate the flowers, and many times had to prove it! Sometimes they would dance, and if questioned about it by curious watchers they would say they danced with the butterflies.

As they grew, so did their imaginations, and by the time they were adults some of their habits seemed strange to others and they were not invited to the other young men's activities. Grandfather advised them to change their ways, to be more serious with life; and because they were obedient boys who loved their parents they tried to heed his advice.

One morning one of the twins told the other of a dream he had had, but before he could finish, the other boy told him the rest of it. This happened many more times and, as they thought it strange, they told the old man about it. The old one told them parts of their dreams were of true things, matters they did not know about because they were not invited to village gatherings. He advised them to make a special visit to a shrine in the moun-

58

tains, to fast and ask guidance. Grandmother made preparations for them, and gave the boys her blessing.

The old ones realized the meaning of the boys' dreams and felt that the twins should commune with the Spirit who was calling them. For a long time they had known that these children they had brought up were possessed with power beyond the natural. Now they could no longer protect them as children, but must let them realize their powers for themselves.

Over many years a wicked man in the village had gained complete control over the people. They were afraid of him, for he was an evil man who was known to have brought about such unexplainable happenings as illness which came suddenly, or even death in those families who resisted him. Fearful unhappiness hung over the whole village.

When the twins returned they told Grandfather what they must do, assuring him they had the protection of the Great One. Then they went to the wicked man and challenged him to a contest of powers. He accepted the challenge and demanded death to the loser!

The twins fasted and prayed, and when the day arrived everyone in the village gathered in the square to watch. The twins appeared in ridiculous costumes. Their bodies were painted in stripes of black and white, and corn husks were tied to their bodies and hair. Deer hoofs, fastened around their ankles, rattled as they walked. The people began to laugh at these good-natured boys, who went right along telling jokes and clowning. The people had not laughed so hard in a long time: they had been afraid to do so. This made the wizard angry, and he shouted that he was ready to begin the contest.

To frighten the people, he commanded the sacred serpent to appear and the **Ava-yunn** came out of the wall of his house! He ordered **Ava-yunn,** the Storm Serpent Old Man, keeper of all bodies of water, to spit out water into an olla set before him and this the serpent did. The wizard took the olla and had the water tested by the people. Then he shouted commands for corn stalks and squash plants to come forth, and the plants appeared! Now, he said, let the twins match his magic if they could.

59

To be a Kossa (Koshare) is a lifetime obligation. Sometimes it is accidental; sometimes it is a wish fulfilled. In the picture it was destined for the twins to become Kossas by powers unknown.

As Old Father might have said, "Each one of us is destined to perform some purpose in our lifetime. Great or small, if we are aware of our senses, we fulfill these deeds successfully."

The cord wisps from the navel of each child tell the purpose or goal each was to reach. Scenes of their earlier life are depicted above the humble home of the grandparents.

With high praise for the wizard, the twins prepared to take their turn. They addressed each other as "Little Brother Before Me," explaining that they did not know which one had come first. The wizard, although flattered by their praise, shouted impatiently for them to get on with the contest.

One of the twins asked the other to get a handful of ashes, explaining again to the people that the other twin must do this because he was the one found in the ashheap. When the boy returned with the ashes, he was ordered by his brother to make a cloud! He tried in vain, then the other twin made a great pretense of trying it himself, and the wizard cried out angrily that they were wasting time.

The twins grew more serious. They began talking in turns of something they could see far away, drawing ever nearer. With words they pictured cloud people approaching out of the distance along a rainbow. The listeners, absorbed and quiet, seemed to fall into a trance of expectancy as the twins talked, and burdens they had lived under for a long time were lifted from them.

At last one twin slapped his palms together and a puff of cloud arose. It flowered into a fog, and suddenly there was a roar of thunder and a flash of lightning. The people heard a singing of beautiful songs, mingled with the sound of raindrops. Through the mist they could see Kachinas dancing. They felt overwhelmed but at peace, and they threw sacred corn meal as an offering of their gratitude for this blessing. As the mist lifted, they saw the Kachinas go away as they had come, leaving with the people messages of hope and peace and happiness. The people knew, with hearts full of humility, that no one else would be blessed in this way.

Then they saw that the wizard was lying dead, struck by lightning, bringing to pass his own penalty of death to the loser!

The twins became great leaders in their village as the years went by. They were the first Koshares. That is why today the Koshares still call each other "Little Brother Before Me", as they appear at ceremonials in their black and white painted stripes, making the people laugh. But the Koshares also play a serious part, for they are summoners of the Kachinas—the supernatural ones, our ancestors. It is also true that the Pueblo Indians, among whom the birth of twins is rare, believed for many years that all such children had supernatural powers. They had customs concerning twins which, along with many of their sacred rites, they prefer not to have written down.

*　　*　　*　　*　　*

Now Old Father said, "There will be no time for stories for awhile; I will be too busy in the fields. Besides—the Great One would not be pleased with me and would not give us good crops if I did not do things at their proper time, and the time for stories is when the snows come."

Index

Ava-yunn, Storm Serpent Old Man (Feathered Serpent), 59

Bandelier National Monument, 13
bear, 29-31
Bear Mountain (Taos Mtns.), 31
bonnet (Cancer), 28, 31
Big Dipper, 31

Cancer (war bonnet), 28
cloud flowers, 37
Cloud Person **(O-ku-wah),** kachina 53-55
cougar, 29-31
coyote, 29-31

Deer Dance, 33
eagle, 30
earthcolor paintings, 14

El Palacio, 14
Endless Trail (Milky Way), 26, 31
e-ve-hanuh, the inner self, 39

"Fathers and Mothers", 28
Faust, 15
Feathered Serpent, **Ava-yunn,** 59
Flint Knife Canyon, west of Santa Clara, 41, 43

Gallup Indian Ceremonial, 13

Gemini, 26, 31

Hancock, D., 15
Hardin, Helen, 14-17
Hardin, Herbert, 14
Hardin, Herbert, jr., 14, 17
headdress, 31
House of the Deer design, 37
kachina, **O-ku-wah,** Cloud Person, 53-55, 62-63

King, Dale Stuart, 13
Koshare, 59, 62-63

Leo, 28, 31
Long Sash (Orion), 15, 25-31
lynx, 36
mano, 14
manta, 47-48
metate, 14

Milky Way (Endless Trail), 26, 31
mole, 28, 30
Mt. Taylor, 31

National Park Service, 13
North Star, 31

O-ku-wah, Cloud Person, kachina, 53-55
Old Father painting, critique of, 14
Old Spider Woman, 28, 41, 43
Orion (Long Sash), 15, 25-31

Palme Academique, French, 13
Philbrook Art Center, 13
Pu-gah-nu-nu, 53-55
Puye, ruins west of Santa Clara, 33, 45, 47, 49

Remus, 15
Romulus, 15

St. Catherine's School, 13
sandals, hide and feather, 42
Sandia Mtns. (Turtle Mtns.), 31
Sangre de Cristo Mtns., 31
Santa Clara, 13, 17
Santa Fe, 13
Santa Fe Indian School, 13
self, inner, **e-ve-hanuh,** 39
Serpent, Feathered, 59
Seton, Ernest Thompson, 13
Shupinna, ruin near Puye, 49
Sipapu, 28
Sipo-pede, 28

snakes, 42
songe-de-ho, goodbye
spider, 29
Spider Woman, Old, 28, 41, 43

Taos Mtns. (Bear Mtn.) 31
Tarzan, 15
Taylor, Mt., 31
Tewa, 13, 17, 28
Turkey Track Mountain, west of Santa Clara, 51
turtle, 30-31
Turtle Mtns. (Sandia Mtns.), 31
Twins (Gemini), 26, 31

Velarde, Herman, 13, 17
Velarde, Marianita Chavarria, 13

warbonnet (Cancer), 28, 31
witch, beautiful, 41
witches, 42-43, 51